CLASSIC JAZZ FOR PIANO

WISE PUBLICATIONS
LONDON/NEW YORK/PARIS/SYDNEY/COPENHAGEN/MADRID

C000093164

EXCLUSIVE DISTRIBUTORS:
MUSIC SALES LIMITED, 8/9 FRITH STREET, LONDON W1V 5TZ.
MUSIC SALES PTY LIMITED, 120 ROTHSCHILD AVENUE, ROSEBERY, NSW 2018, AUSTRALIA.

ORDER NO.AM944735. ISBN 0-7119-6667-2

PRINTED IN THE UNITED KINGDOM BY REDWOOD BOOKS LIMITED, TROWBRIDGE, WILTSHIRE.

YOUR GUARANTEE OF QUALITY
AS PUBLISHERS, WE STRIVE TO PRODUCE EVERY BOOK TO THE HIGHEST COMMERCIAL STANDARDS.
THE BOOK HAS BEEN CAREFULLY DESIGNED TO MINIMISE AWKWARD PAGE TURNS AND TO MAKE PLAYING FROM IT A REAL PLEASURE.
PARTICULAR CARE HAS BEEN GIVEN TO SPECIFYING ACID FREE, NEUTRAL-SIZED PAPER MADE FROM PULPS WHICH HAVE NOT BEEN ELEMENTAL CHLORINE BLEACHED.
THIS PULP IS FROM FARMED SUSTAINABLE FORESTS AND WAS PRODUCED WITH SPECIAL REGARD FOR THE ENVIRONMENT.
THROUGHOUT THE PRINTING AND BINDING HAVE BEEN PLANNED TO ENSURE A STURDY, ATTRACTIVE PUBLICATION WHICH SHOULD GIVE YEARS OF ENJOYMENT.
IF YOUR COPY FAILS TO MEET OUR HIGH STANDARDS, PLEASE INFORM US AND WE WILL GLADLY REPLACE IT.

MUSIC SALES' COMPLETE CATALOGUE DESCRIBES THOUSANDS OF TITLES AND IS AVAILABLE IN FULL COLOUR SECTIONS, BY SUBJECT, DIRECT FROM MUSIC SALES LIMITED.
PLEASE STATE YOUR AREAS OF INTEREST AND SEND A CHEQUE/POSTAL ORDER FOR £1.50 FOR POSTAGE TO:
MUSIC SALES LIMITED, NEWMARKET ROAD, BURY ST. EDMUNDS, SUFFOLK IP33 3YB.

VISIT THE INTERNET MUSIC SHOP AT HTTP://WWW.MUSICSALES.CO.UK

A FOGGY DAY

MUSIC & LYRICS BY GEORGE GERSHWIN & IRA GERSHWIN.

Moderately, with a strong beat

ANTHROPOLOGY

BY DIZZY GILLESPIE & CHARLIE PARKER.
© COPYRIGHT 1948 CONSOLIDATED MUSIC PUBLISHERS INCORPORATED.
BOSWORTH & COMPANY LIMITED, 14-18 HEDDON STREET, LONDON W1.
ALL RIGHTS RESERVED. INTERNATIONAL COPYRIGHT SECURED.

Moderate Be Bop tempo

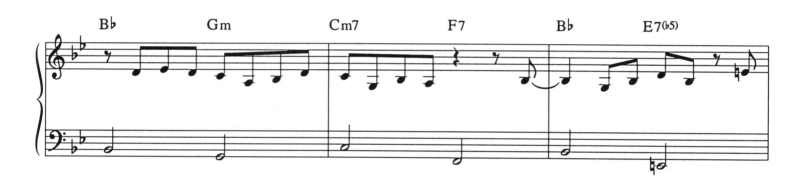

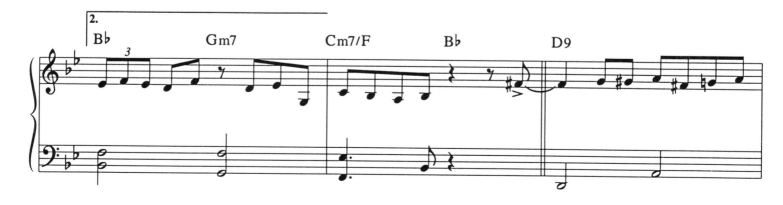

A NIGHT IN TUNISIA

MUSIC BY FRANK PAPARELLI & JOHN 'DIZZY' GILLESPIE. WORDS BY RAYMOND LEVEEN.
© COPYRIGHT 1944 & 1960 MCA MUSIC (A DIVISION OF MCA INCORPORATED, USA).
MCA MUSIC LIMITED, 77 FULHAM PALACE ROAD, LONDON W6 FOR THE WORLD (EXCLUDING NORTH, SOUTH AND CENTRAL AMERICA, JAPAN, AUSTRALASIA AND THE PHILIPPINES).
ALL RIGHTS RESERVED. INTERNATIONAL COPYRIGHT SECURED.

EMBRACEABLE YOU

MUSIC & LYRICS BY GEORGE GERSHWIN & IRA GERSHWIN.

FASCINATING RHYTHM

MUSIC & LYRICS BY GEORGE GERSHWIN & IRA GERSHWIN.

I GOT RHYTHM

MUSIC & LYRICS BY GEORGE GERSHWIN & IRA GERSHWIN.

I'M BEGINNING TO SEE THE LIGHT

WORDS & MUSIC BY HARRY JAMES, DUKE ELLINGTON, JOHNNY HODGES & DON GEORGE.
© COPYRIGHT 1944 GRAND MUSIC CORPORATION, USA.
CAMPBELL CONNELLY & COMPANY LIMITED, 8/9 FRITH STREET, LONDON W1.

IS YOU IS, OR IS YOU AIN'T (MA' BABY)

WORDS & MUSIC BY BILLY AUSTIN & LOUIS JORDAN.

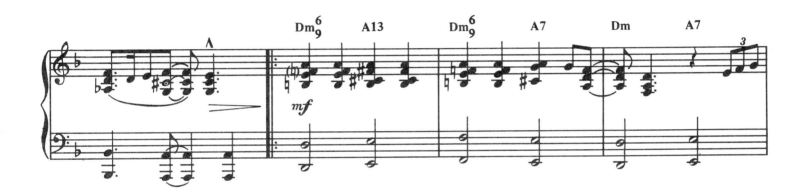

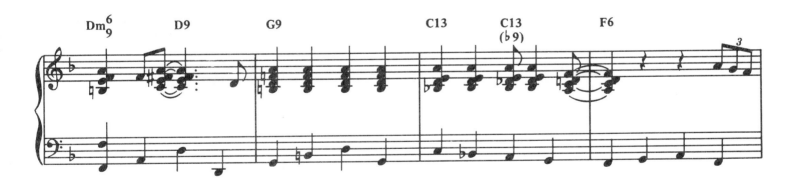

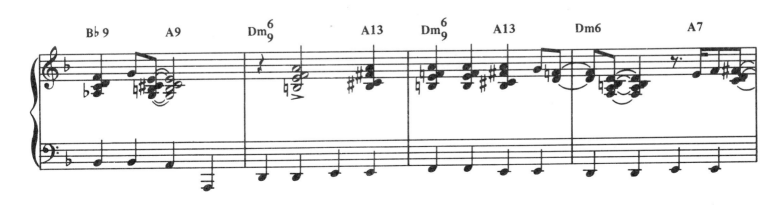

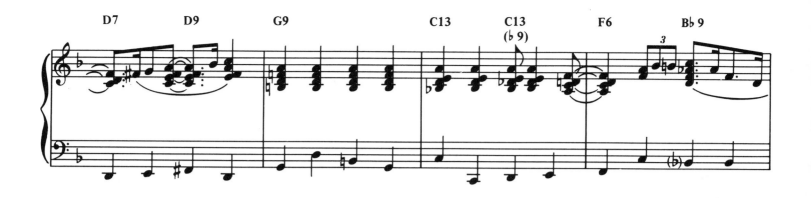

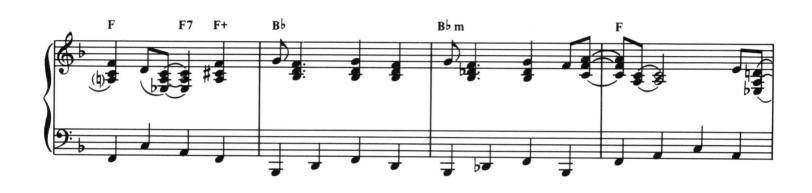

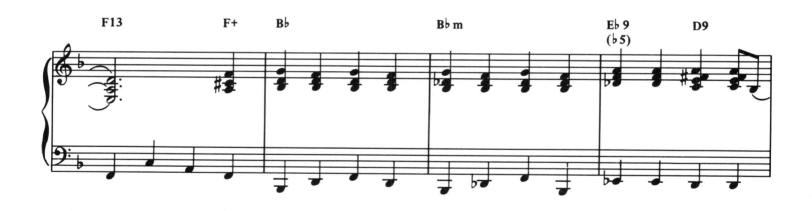

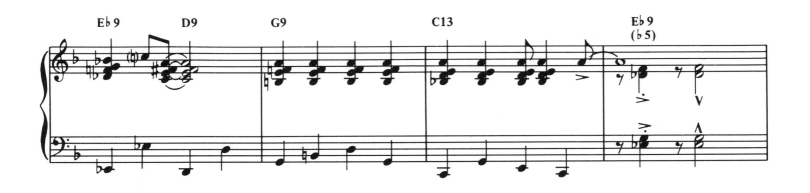

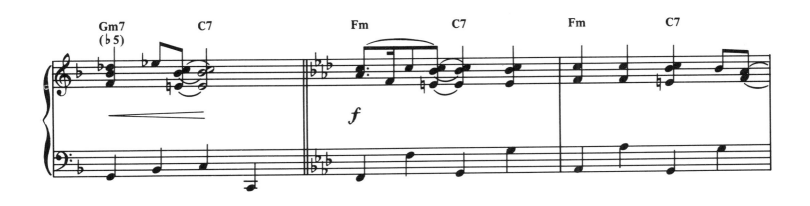

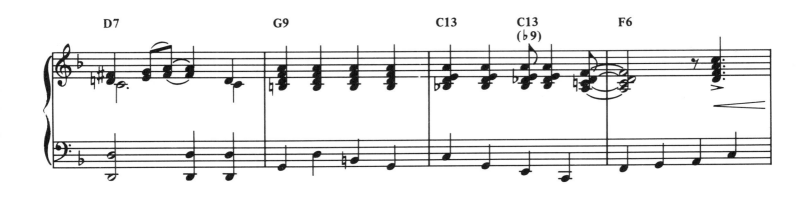

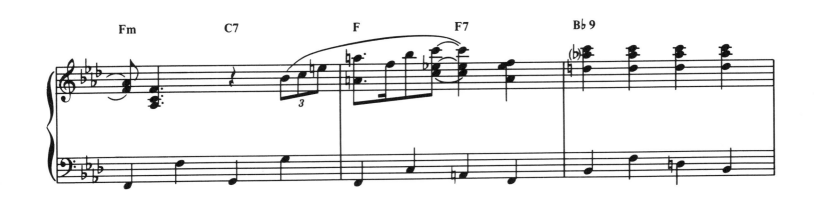

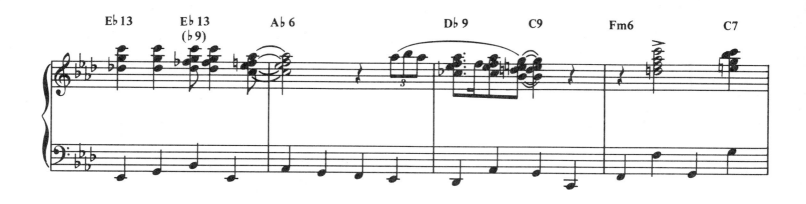

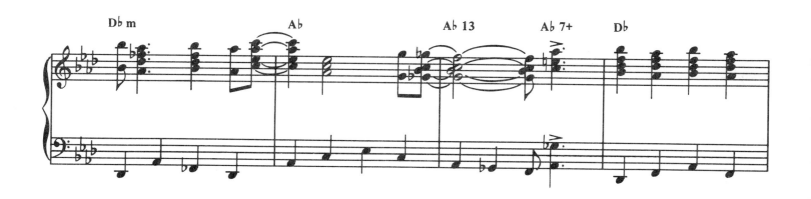

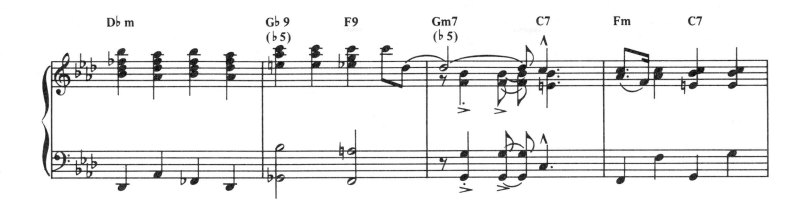

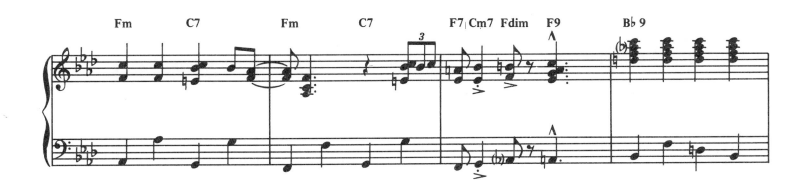

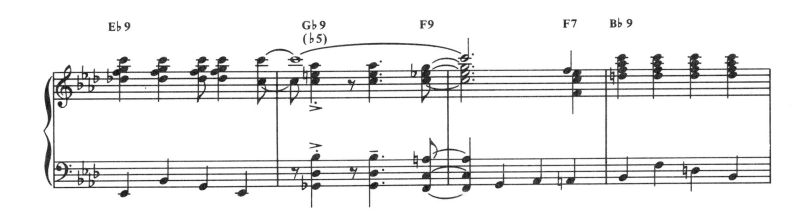

IT AIN'T NECESSARILY SO
(FROM "PORGY AND BESS")

WORDS & MUSIC BY GEORGE GERSHWIN, DUBOSE & DOROTHY HEYWARD & IRA GERSHWIN.
© COPYRIGHT 1935 (RENEWED) CHAPPELL & COMPANY, USA. THIS ARRANGEMENT © COPYRIGHT 1997 CHAPPELL & COMPANY, USA.
WARNER CHAPPELL MUSIC LIMITED, 129 PARK STREET, LONDON W1.
ALL RIGHTS RESERVED. INTERNATIONAL COPYRIGHT SECURED.

LULLABY OF BIRDLAND

MUSIC BY GEORGE SHEARING. WORDS BY GEORGE DAVID WEISS.

Medium tempo

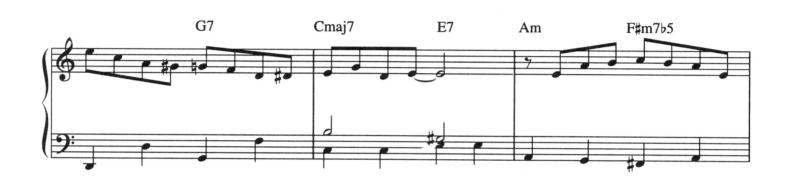

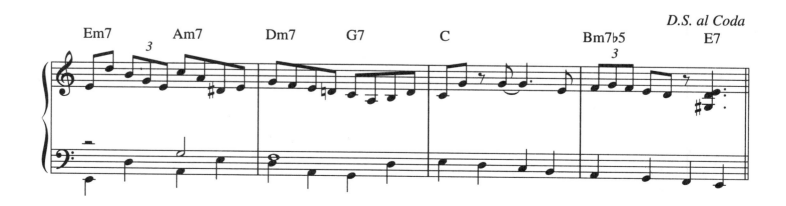

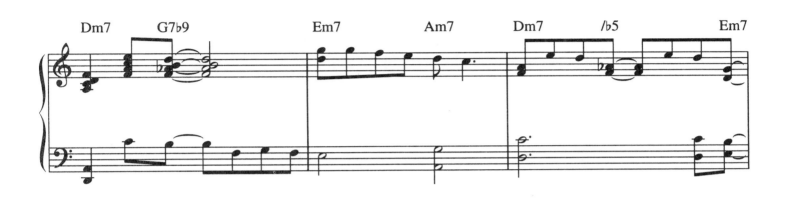

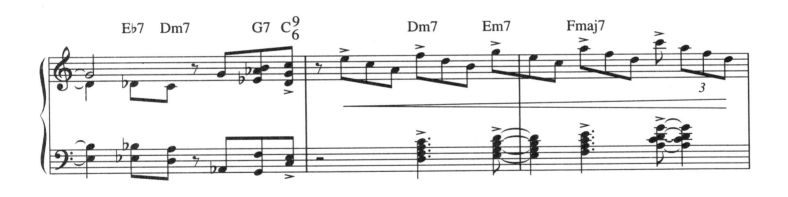

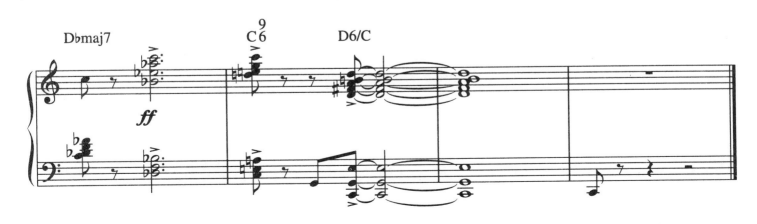

MONK'S MOOD

BY THELONIOUS MONK.

NICE WORK IF YOU CAN GET IT

MUSIC & LYRICS BY GEORGE GERSHWIN & IRA GERSHWIN.

PERDIDO

MUSIC BY JUAN TIZOL. WORDS BY HARRY LENK AND ERVIN DRAKE.
© COPYRIGHT 1942 TEMPO MUSIC INCORPORATED, USA.
CAMPBELL CONNELLY & COMPANY LIMITED, 8/9 FRITH STREET, LONDON W1.
ALL RIGHTS RESERVED. INTERNATIONAL COPYRIGHT SECURED.

Medium swing tempo

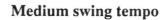

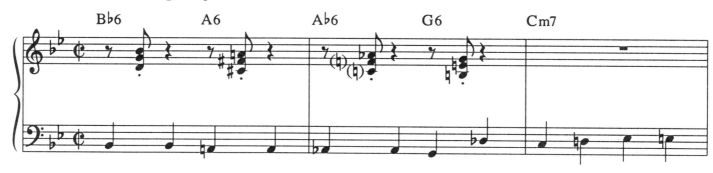

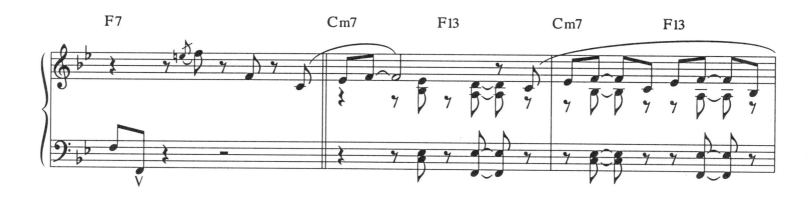

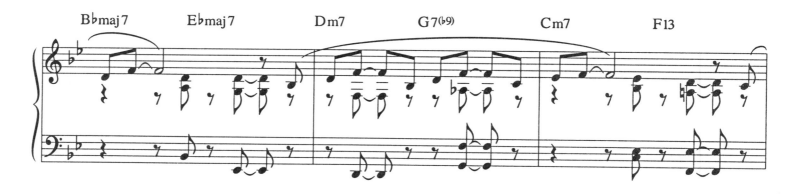

SOPHISTICATED LADY

WORDS BY IRVING MILLS & MITCHELL PARISH. MUSIC BY DUKE ELLINGTON.

Moderately

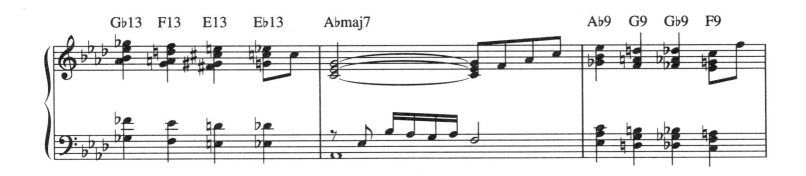

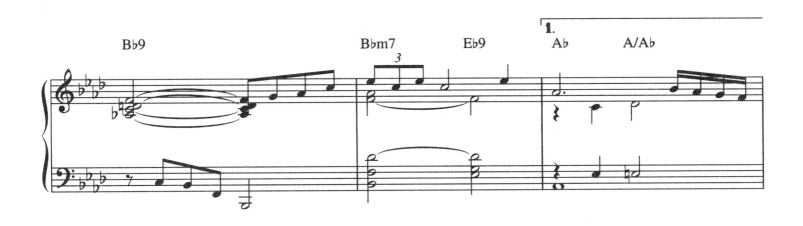

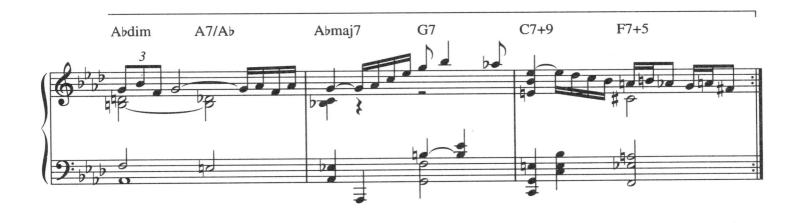

SLIGHTLY OUT OF TUNE (DESAFINADO)

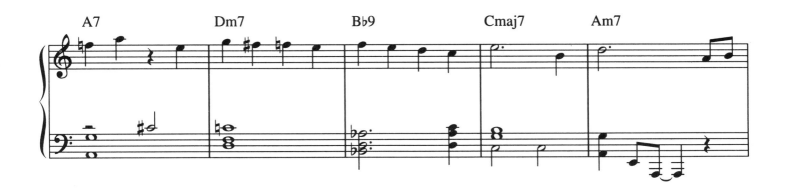

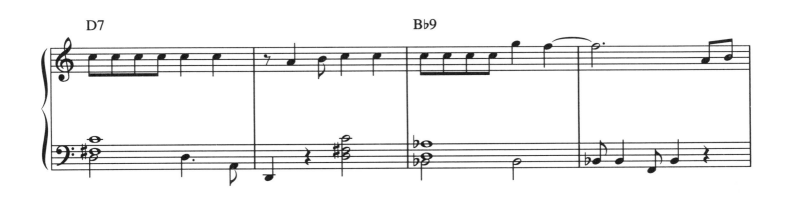

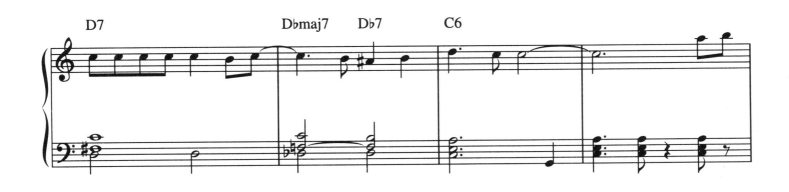

SUMMERTIME (FROM "PORGY AND BESS")

BY GEORGE GERSHWIN, IRA GERSHWIN, DUBOSE & DOROTHY HEYWARD.

THE GIRL FROM IPANEMA (GAROTA DE IPANEMA)

ORIGINAL WORDS BY VINICIUS DE MORAES. ENGLISH LYRIC BY NORMAN GIMBEL. MUSIC BY ANTONIO CARLOS JOBIM.

THEY CAN'T TAKE THAT AWAY FROM ME

MUSIC & LYRICS BY GEORGE GERSHWIN & IRA GERSHWIN.